Revelation 21:3

And I heard a loud voice from the throne saying: "Behold, the dwelling place of God is with man, and He will live with them. They will be His people, and God Himself will be with them as their God.

The Second Jewish Temple. Model in the Israel Museum.

Jerusalem was the site of two historical temples. The first was built by King Solomon and destroyed by King Nebuchadnessar of Babylon in 586 BC. The second temple was refurbished and expanded upon by Herod the Great and was destroyed by the Romans during a Jewish revolt in 70 AD. The second temple lasted for a total of 585 years (516 BC to 70 AD).

Read this verse with understanding. God is stating, "Because you have allowed these "detestable and abdominal" things to come into my temple...my "sanctuary" or the holiest place in the temple...."

Wherefore, as I live, saith the Lord GOD; Surely, because thou hast defiled my sanctuary with all thy detestable things, and with all thine abominations, therefore will I also diminish thee; neither shall mine eye spare, neither will I have any pity.

Ezekiel 5:11

Today, a "temple" might not take on the shape it once did centuries ago. A modern "temple" may look something more like an embassy. For example, the American Embassy in Baghdad, Iraq is our nation's largest and most expensive embassy in the world. Encompassing 104 acres, this massive compound is nearly as large as Vatican City.

U.S. Embassy compound in Baghdad's Green Zone

In scripture, "Temple" and "Sanctuary" are often used interchangeably. There are slight yet precise differences. A temple is a building devoted to worship or regarded as a dwelling place of a god or gods or other objects of religious reverence. A sanctuary is noted as being the holiest part of a temple or church – usually where a high altar is found.

48"However, the Most High does not dwell in temples made with hands, as the prophet says:

49' Heaven *is* My throne,
And earth *is* My footstool.
What house will you build for Me? says the Lord,
Or what *is* the place of My rest?

Acts 7:48-49

The God who made the world and everything in it is the Lord of heaven and earth and does not live in temples made by human hands.

Acts 17:24

Jesus, son of the living God, came in the flesh to teach us about matters concerning the "spirit" – the HOLY SPIRIT. He came at the directive of God the Father. He is God incarnate, the Word made flesh. His purpose, - to draw men to himself and to announce the coming kingdom of God on earth. His reasons were redemption, reconciliation, and restoration.

He made it a point to teach and instruct people in matters of the spirit telling them,***"You however, are not controlled by the flesh, but by the Spirit, if the Spirit of God lives in you. If anyone does not have my spirit, he does not belong to me. "Romans 8:9***

The Holy Spirit descended on the believers gathered in the upper room. They waited, as instructed by Jesus, for his Holy Spirit. Fire, seemingly shaped like "tongues," filled the room and descended upon those gathered. This was Pentecost. God's Holy Spirit entered into the temple of the human body to dwell with and IN believers. (**Acts 2:3-4**)

Jesus instructed men and women teaching them and saying, ***"Do you not know that your body is a temple of the Holy Spirit who is in you, whom you have received from God? You are not your own; you were bought at a price. Therefore, glorify God with your body."***

1 Corinthians 6:19

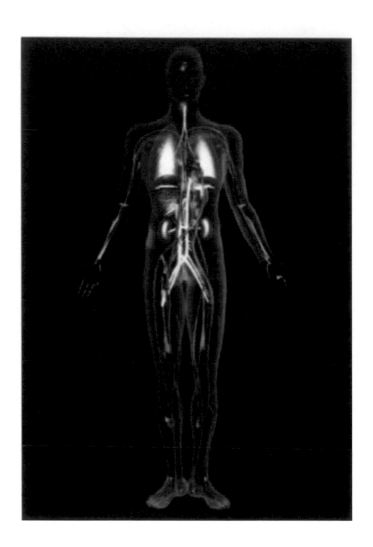

"And what agreement has the temple of God with idols? For you are the temple of the living God; as God has said, I will dwell in them, and walk in them; and I will be their God, and they shall be my people."

2 Corinthians 6:16

Wat Samphran aka Dragon Temple - Bangkok

Water of Life Discourse

Wikipedia

A Samaritan woman came to draw water, and Jesus said to her, "Give me a drink." (His disciples had gone to the city to buy food.) The Samaritan woman said to him, "How is it that you, a Jew, ask a drink of me, a woman of Samaria?" (Jews do not share things in common with Samaritans.) Jesus answered her, "If you knew the gift of God, and who it is that is saying to you, 'Give me a drink', you would have asked him, and he would have given you living water." The woman said to him, "Sir, you have no bucket, and the well is deep. Where do you get that living water? Are you greater than our ancestor Jacob, who gave us the well, and with his sons and his flocks drank from it?" Jesus said to her, "Everyone who drinks of this water will be thirsty again, but those who drink of the water that I will give them will never be thirsty. The water that I will give will become in them a spring of water gushing up to eternal life." The woman said to him, "Sir, give me this water, so that I may never be thirsty or have to keep coming here to draw water."

Jesus said to her, "Go, call your husband, and come back." The woman answered him, "I have no husband." Jesus said to her, "You are right in saying, 'I have no husband'; for you have had five husbands, and the man you are now living with is not your husband. What you have said is true!" The woman said to him, "Sir, I see that you are a prophet. Our ancestors worshipped on this mountain, but you say that the place where people must worship is in Jerusalem." Jesus said to her, **"Woman, believe me, the hour is coming when you will worship the Father neither on this mountain nor in Jerusalem.** You worship what you do not know; we worship what we know, for salvation is from the Jews.

But the hour is coming, and is now here, when the true worshippers will worship the Father in spirit and truth, for the Father seeks such as these to worship him. God is spirit, and those who worship him must worship in spirit and truth." The woman said to him, "I know that Messiah is coming" (who is called Christ). "When he comes, he will proclaim all things to us." Jesus said to her, "I am he, the one who is speaking to you."

Jesus made it a point to tell this woman that TRUE worship will come from within the human believer to God directly. A time was coming when people would not need to trek to a temple/building to worship God. A structure built with human hands would not contain the Holy Spirit of God – with God, it's personal.

Only a sanctified human being, submitted to Him in humbleness, repentant, reverent and renewed, is a vessel (a "sanctuary" or most Holy place) capable of being filled with God's spirit to receive from Him instruction and guidance in how to worship Him in spirit and truth.

Jesus had to teach these things to his disciples and many others as well. As He left the temple and was walking away His disciples came up to Him to point out its buildings adorned with beautiful stones and consecrated gifts. Jesus said to them, **_"As for what you see here, the time will come when not one stone will be left on another; every one will be thrown down."Luke 21:5 and Matthew 24:1_**

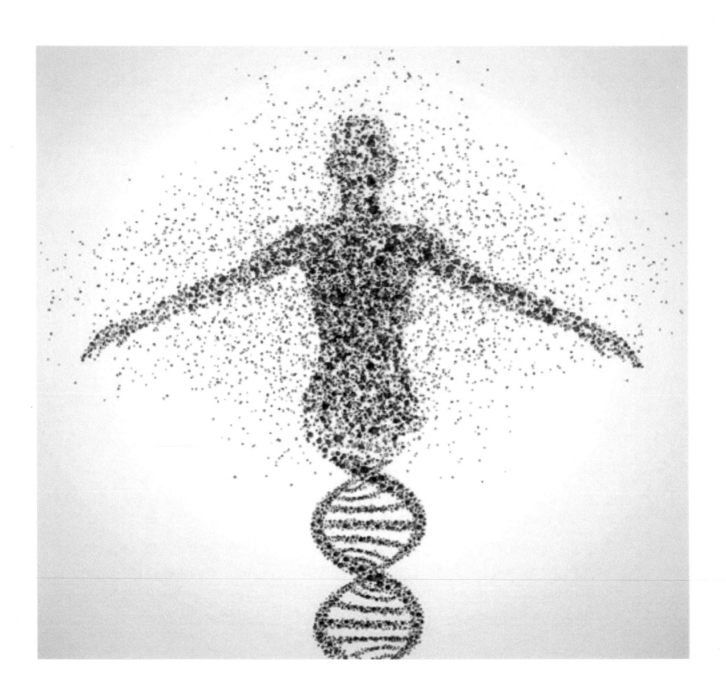

"Do you not know that your body is a temple of the Holy Spirit who is in you, whom you have received from God? You are not your own. You were bought at a price. Therefore, glorify God with your body."

1 Corinthians 6:19

The abomination that causes desolation, spoken of in the Bible, is the infiltration and domination of the human body by way of technological and biological agents. Science will dictate and rule over the human body. Technology will be enthroned at the particulate level. Manipulation of the mRNA and DNA "code" will restructure the human genome to change God's original design. God will not dwell in a "temple made with human hands."

The world is rushing to bring to market an "antigen" to combat a biological threat currently plaguing humanity. It professes to have a remedy for this deadly pathogen. This will result in a micro needle array patch delivery system - it's very design taken from the fangs of a serpent.

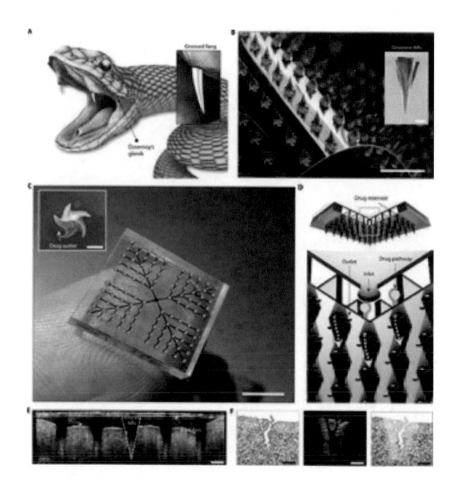

Snake fang–inspired stamping patch for transdermal delivery of liquid formulations

PDF: https://stm.sciencemag.org/content/11/503/eaaw3329.abstract

We have pointed out to many that evil sits enthroned in the "temple of technology" – the word "TECHNOLOGY" or "TECHNE" in the Greek means: **"science of the craft"** or **"sleight of hand"**

https://www.latimes.com/archives/la-xpm-2001-dec-09-bk-fraphael9-story.html

https://plato.stanford.edu/entries/episteme-techne/

https://www.thoughtco.com/techne-rhetoric-1692457

https://www.lexico.com/en/definition/techne

We have pointed out that satan has copied God's construct of the man made "temple" to closely resemble what we today can clearly identify as a computer/quantum chip. He now sits "enthroned" in the temple of technology. We don't call it the "BEAST SYSTEM" without reason.

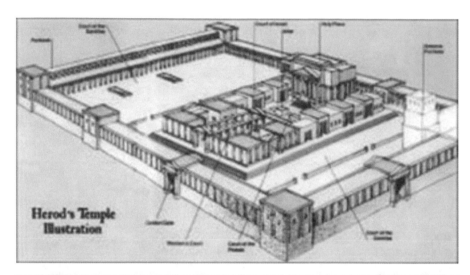

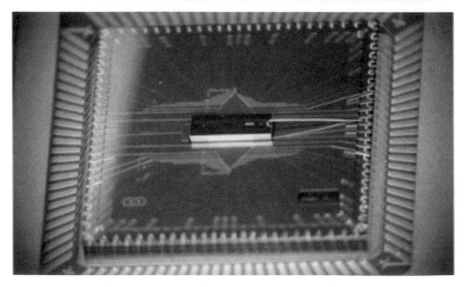

The Jews demanded of Jesus, "What sign can you show us to prove your authority to do these things?" Jesus answered, "Destroy this temple, and in three days I will raise it up again!" "This temple took forty-six years to build!" The Jews replied. "You are going to raise it up in three days?" But Jesus was speaking about the temple of his body.

John 2:18-21

The temple in which God resides is found within men. Jesus made that perfectly clear. This can be seen and understood only through the Holy Spirit. If you can't see all of this, ask God to help you.

Much has been made and spoken of the "mark of the beast." If we take our commonly used reference to computers (the beast) and look deeper – we can see why. Computers are satan's physical outworking – his instruments – brought about by his speaking to the minds of those men and women committed to furthering his dominion. Computer technology is wrought with terminology acknowledging his "sovereignty" i.e.) **Security Administrator Tool for Analyzing Networks** (**SATAN**) or **Mailer Daemon** which actually comes from the Greek language, meaning an "inner or attendant spirit".

Soon, men will have to choose. A "cure" is coming. A global ***recipe*** for this micro needle array patch has been provided to pharmaceutical companies around the world to produce and distribute a nucleic acid vaccine (DNA or RNA). A link to a list of companies is provided in this magazine.

An excerpt from Pathways to Peace Ministries states:

*Revelation chapter 18 gives a description of the fall of Babylon and in verse 23 it gives us the reason why all nations were deceived. This may be shocking for many people. Let's read what the Bible says. Referring to the fall of Babylon Revelation 18:23 says "And the light of a candle shall shine no more at all in thee; and the voice of the bridegroom and of the bride shall be heard no more at all in thee: for thy merchants were the great men of the earth; for by thy **sorceries** were all nations deceived."*

By the "sorceries" of Babylon all nations were deceived. *The Greek word for "sorceries" in verse 23 is "pharmakeia"[far-mak-i'-ah]. According to the Thayer Greek Dictionary "pharmakeia" is "the use or administering of drugs; poisoning; and sorcery, magical arts, often found in connection with idolatry and fostered by it. " If you put the original Greek word "pharmakeia" in place of the English word "sorceries" the end of verse 23 would say, " For by thy **pharmakeia** were ALL nations deceived"! "Pharmakeia" is where we get our English word "pharmacy"! Pharmacy is a well organized and professionalized system that administers poisonous drugs. The Bible reveals that Babylon will deceive all nations by the use of pharmacy that is in connection to "magical arts" and idolatry. "Magical arts" has its deep roots in witchcraft and the occultic world. We don't have to do a deep Bible study to know that Satan is directly behind the magical arts and God's people should have nothing to do with it. Professed deceived Christians today use "magical arts" under the disguise of contemplative prayer, "christian" humanism, and spiritual formation. In general those involved in sorcery, witchcraft, and magic are known to use "magic" potions to "heal", deceive, poison, control, or kill someone.*

Pharmacy mainly uses a mixture of toxic chemicals, metals, and/or synthetic elements to produce "pharmaceuticals" that are designed to manipulate the biochemistry or metabolic functions of the body in an attempt to get a "desired" affect in the treatment of a disease or sickness.

In other words, pharmacy mixes up different types of poison, package it, patent it,and claims that it can treat certain types of diseases. The main problem with that system is that poison is poison. Pharmaceutical drugs are poisonous. When poison is put into the body it has negative effects on the entire body system from head to toe. These are not just "side effects" or "unintended" sicknesses or diseases that a person suffers as a result of using a drug. These are "direct effects" because the reality is that drugs have direct effects on the entire body system including the brain. When you go back to Revelation 18:23, Jesus uses the Greek word "pharmakeia" to reveal to us the main thing that will be used to deceive ALL people in the last days is a well organized system of administering poisonous drugs to billions of people that are not only toxic to the organs of body, but have direct negative effects on the brain. Many of these drugs used for a variety of reasons are known to cause problems with memory, mood, and contribute to negative personality changes.

Who is the main one behind the system of pharmacy and the administering of poisonous drugs that Babylon uses to deceive all nations? A logo or symbol reveals the values and the purpose of a business, organization, or professional occupation. They use a logo or symbol as an identifying "mark" to the world. In other words, that logo makes a direct link to a business or occupation. When a person thinks of the "swoosh" they immediately think of the Nike corporation. The symbols and logos of modern medicine clearly reveal who is behind the scenes orchestrating the whole system of the administering of poisonous drugs that manipulate the bodies and minds of billions of people around the world. Let's just look at three recognizable symbols and unmask the truth!

Read the entire commentary here:

https://www.pathwaytopeace.net/index.php/blogs-and-articles/pharmakeia-deception

The mark of the beast, in a modern context, is a micro needle array patch delivery system. Contained within this patch are a multitude of "potions" and an invisible, traceable mark will be left in the skin identifying those who have been inoculated and thus deemed "safe" to be in and amongst society. The "mark" will be of a bioluminescent material (enzyme) known as **LUCIFER**ase.

Luciferase is a generic term for the class of oxidative enzymes that produce bioluminescence, and is usually distinguished from a photoprotein. The name was first used by Raphaël Dubois who invented the words luciferin and luciferase, for the substrate and enzyme, respectively. Wikipedia

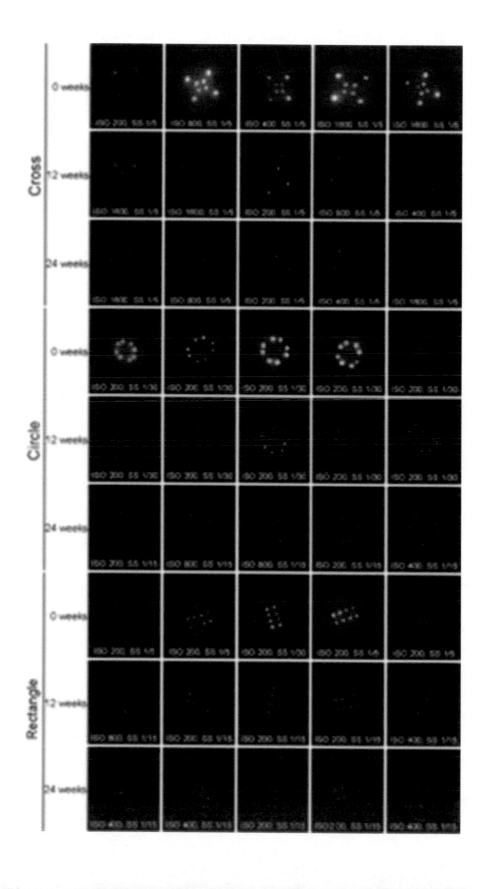

This micro needle array or "nucleic acid vaccine" will dispense not only a luminescent traceable tattoo, but introduce an entirely new technological and biological "system" into the human body that will immediately begin "rewiring" via an mRNA replication process aspects of the human genome thus transforming a person's God-given DNA to a "made-with-human-hands" molecular construct. Helping aid in this transformation is the next-generation mobile phone system to be known going forward as IMT-2020 instead of "fifth generation mobile network".

See more information on FRET – Forster Resonance Energy Transfer

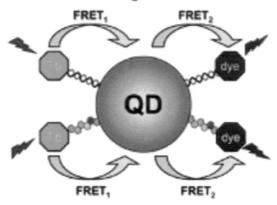

Scheme 1. FRET Relays: Terbium Complexes and Dyes (Both Conjugated with Peptides or Oligonucleotides) are Coassembled on the Same QD^a

^{a}"Pulsed excitation in UV leads to excited terbium and QD and prompt FRET from QD to dye (FRET$_2$). After a delay of several microseconds, there is still much terbium in the excited state, whereas the QD has decayed to its ground state, and efficient time-delayed FRET from terbium to QD (FRET$_1$) becomes possible. The newly excited QD can then sensitize again the dyes by TG FRET$_2$.

Förster resonance energy transfer, fluorescence resonance energy transfer, resonance energy transfer or electronic energy transfer is a mechanism describing energy transfer between two light-sensitive molecules. <u>Wikipedia</u>

Please see:

Lanthanides and Quantum Dots as Förster Resonance Energy Transfer Agents for Diagnostics and Cellular Imaging

<u>https://pubs.acs.org/doi/abs/10.1021/ic4017883</u>

This soon-to-be-released nucleic acid "vaccine" will also connect the human being to the block chain system by way of the Internet of Things. This will grant them access to the new digital monetary system that is slated to be in place once the economies of the world collapse and a worldwide reset ensues.

We hope that you find the material presented in this month's magazine thought provoking, soul-searching, and a confirmation of what it written to us in scripture.

The anti-christ beast system IS being revealed to this generation. Its destructive spirit permeates technology and science (TECHNE - Def. Greek: "science of the craft" and "sleight of hand").

But I saw no temple in the city because the Lord God Almighty and the Lamb are its temple. The city has no need of sun or moon to shine on it because the glory of God illuminates the city and the Lamb is its lamp.

Rev. 21:22

The following represents a body of evidence and testimony from scientific sources regarding SARS-CoV-2. It is comprised of published peer reviewed papers, and transcripts of interviews of medical professionals. Additionally, one each from President Donald Trump and Prime Minister Benjamin Netanyahu. A glossary of terms is included for easy reference. In conclusion, links to several media reports and additional peer reviewed published papers, and to our weekly Livestreams appearing within the messaging area of our Patreon site, are included for your continued research.

The primary focus here is two-fold. First and foremost, the spiritual ramifications of the technologies presented herein. Second, citatation of HIV genomes within the RNA genomic sequence of SARS-CoV-2, coupled with direct evidence of and testimony to the permanent alteration of host DNA by administration of either a DNA-based, or RNA-based vaccine. Both, exhibiting the same results.

Please reference our previous publications of Entangled magazine, specifically, the June and July, 2020 editions outlining the foundational research of the technologies resulting in the manufacturing, distribution and administration of a vaccine-based mark of the beast. In its entirety of three-plus years in publication, the information contained within its pages coalesce to this time.

Extensive explanations, providing Biblical context to these technologies, are presented in our thrice-weekly, two-hour Livestreams broadcast over the course of three years. Those broadcast during July, 2020 are linked near the end of this month's publication.

The spiritual cannot be separated from the physical so long as we exist in human form.

May God Bless you and yours

Anthony and Kathleen Patch

Link Livestream
Thursday 7pm Eastern 7/30/2020:
"The Abomination That Causes Desolation"

https://youtu.be/uv3poZH2SiM

President Trump: "We Have The Military All Lined Up" (re: Vaccine Video)

July 31, 2020 at 8:30

Excerpt of Video Transcript: (please see below, article previously posted re: the IDF and vaccinations in Israel)

one issue that has come up is once you

35:54 do have a

35:55 vaccine how do you properly distribute

35:58 it

35:59 how do you get it out quickly when we

36:01 have the vaccine we have the military

36:03 all lined up

36:04 and the military is going to be doing it

36:07 in a very powerful manner these are

36:10 people that don't usually do vaccines

36:12 they do soldiers and they do lots of

36:14 other things that frankly are

36:16 more difficult but we have a general

36:19 and logistically he's all set

Coronavirus czar debuts 'Shield of Israel' strategic plan.

Excerpts:

"I expect all government ministers to back up this plan," Netanyahu said. "I expect all Israeli citizens, without exception, to cooperate with it. Together, we will defeat coronavirus."

With regards to "test, trace, isolate," the methodology that experts believe is key to stopping the spread of the pandemic, Gamzu admitted that until now the Health Ministry has not done a sufficient job. As such, "the IDF will deal with this," he said.

"The IDF's involvement is very important because it is a system that can work quickly," Gamzu said.

My Comment: Expect this here in the USA. (July 28)

Could Retroviruses Play a Role in COVID-19?

By Dr. Joseph Mercola

Mercola.com

May 4, 2020

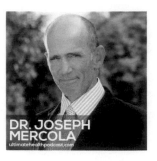

Dr. Judy Mikovits, Ph.D. is a cellular and molecular biologist,[1]researcher and was the founding research director of the Whittemore Peterson Institute that researches and treats chronic fatigue syndrome (CFS) in Reno, Nevada.

She is likely one of the most qualified scientists in the world to comment on this disease because of her groundbreaking research in molecular biology and virology.

One of the most shocking revelations Mikovits reveals is that she doesn't believe SARS-CoV-2 is the cause of COVID-19 but merely serves to activate or wake up a dormant XMRV infection. To support her assertion, she states that COVID-19 patients have the same cytokine signature as the gammaretrovirus XMRV, which she published many years ago.

XMRV stands for "xenotropic murine leukemia virus-related virus." Xenotrophic refers to viruses that only replicate in cells other than those of the host species. So, XMRVs are viruses that infect human cells yet are not human viruses.2

The XMRV retrovirus is actually the virus that has the same cytokine storm signature as COVID-19, not coronaviruses, which are far more benign. (I delve into what retroviruses are in another section further below.)

Additionally, there may be other infections that also are contributing to the infection, such as Borelia and Babesia or parasites, which may be why some of the antiparasite drugs like Ivermectin and hydroxychloroquine are working.

Getting back to the issue of gammaretroviruses, Mikovits research showed that many of our vaccines are contaminated with them. How did this happen? In short, vaccine viruses were replicated and grown in animal cell cultures that were already contaminated with retroviruses. In other words, the root of the problem stems from the use of contaminated cell culture lines.

Mikovits goes even further, explaining that, "It became clear in 2011 that these [gammaretro]viruses had adapted to become aerosolized." This is a rather shocking finding, and this, Mikovits says, is what allows the gammaretroviruses to spread in laboratories from one cell line to another.

Lab workers may also be inadvertently spreading them as they are using cell lines contaminated with retroviruses in vaccine production that could result in the spread of these retroviruses via the finished vaccine. Mikovits suspects COVID-19 may in fact be a type of vaccine-derived or vaccine-induced retroviral infection.

"I don't believe [COVID-19] is infection from without," she says. "I believe the spread across [210] countries4is from injection, and there's enough evidence to support that."

SARS-CoV-2 — A Combination of SARS, Gammaretroviruses and HIV

Another of her theories is that SARS-CoV-2 is unlikely to have had a zoonotic origin but is likely synthetically produced. She believes it originated in and escaped or leaked from a biosafety laboratory. Mikovits believes both scenarios might be at play, where a lab-created virus, SARS-CoV-2, is causing serious infection and/or death only in those who have underlying retroviruses in their bodies.

Mikovits suspects that people who do not have retroviral infections, SARS-CoV-2 causes no or only mild symptoms. Another possibility is that the SARS-CoV-2 virus is the result of growing coronaviruses in retrovirus-contaminated cell lines, producing a gammaretrovirus-carrying virus. According to Mikovits, her 2009 through 2011 work suggested 25 million to 30 million Americans were carriers of XMRVs and other gammaretroviruses. That estimate is over a decade old now so the number is likely far higher.

"There is a family of gammaretroviruses, most likely [in] contaminated blood supply and vaccines that are still to this day, almost 10 years later, being injected," she says.

"We don't need an infectious virus if you inject the blueprint, if you inject the provirus. And ... there are a lot of data to support COVID-19 is not SARS-CoV-2 alone, that it's SARS-CoV-2and XMRVs (human gammaretroviruses) and HIV."

Might Wearing a Mask Worsen Your Odds of Illness?

Mikovits is also highly critical of the recommendation (and in some places mandate) to wear a face mask or fabric cover such as a bandana around your face. She believes:

"Wearing a mask is going to cause more secretions and give more cells a home and amplify any viruses. [Wearing a mask is] immune suppressive; it's going to limit your body's ability to produce Type 1 interferon.

You're driving the infection in yourself and you're not preventing the spread. [Instead], you're amplifying [replication of] not just [SARS-CoV-2] but also many other [viruses], including your XMRVs, influenza or other dormant viruses.

What keeps those dormant viruses dormant? Your natural killer (NK) cells, your mast cells, your macrophages. That's where you're getting the inflammatory signature.

So, every virus you amplify is driving the inflammatory signature, and you're going to get sick. [The resulting illness] doesn't have to be SARS-CoV-2 at all. You're making yourself sick [by bringing dormant viruses out of dormancy]. It's insanity."

Wearing a face mask after getting a live flu vaccine may further worsen your odds, she says. Why? Because you're injecting three or more live flu virus strains into your body, which lowers your immune function. You're also going to shed the viruses contained in the vaccine. If you wear a mask, Mikovits says, you'll shed those viruses into the mask, which could encourage illness.

Why PCR Testing Is Bad

We're also being lied to about the prevalence of infection. We're seeing inflated case numbers for the simple reason that the Centers for Disease Control and Prevention no longer requires doctors to do testing in order to confirm that a patient is in fact infected with SARS-CoV-2 or died from COVID-19. The numbers now include "suspected" and "assumed" cases.

What's more, the initial decision to use RT-PCR (reverse transcription polymerase chain reaction) testing instead of antibody testing was an unwise one, as it virtually guaranteed an overestimation of the problem. RT-PCR is now being used to diagnose an active infection by detecting the presence of SARS-CoV-2 genetic material.5However, by doing that, you end up with high rates of false positives. Mikovits explains how the RT-PCR test works:

Convergys® POC RT-PCR COVID-19 Detection Kit

for Convergys® POC RT-PCR Nucleic Acid Detection System

- Qualitative detection of the novel coronavirus SARS-CoV-2
- Real-time PCR methodology
- Targets specific nucleotide sequences of SARS-CoV-2
- Cartridge based kit for use with the fully-automated Convergys® POC RT-PCR System
- Results within 90 minutes

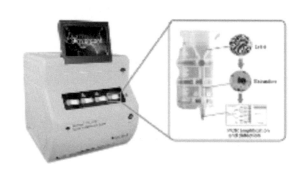

"We're taking a swab and scraping some epithelial cells [from the back of the sinuses or throat] because that's what coronaviruses infect ... We get a little RNA — because it's an RNA virus — we reverse-transcribe that, meaning write it backwards with enzymes in the lab, and then we amplify it [through a] polymerase chain reaction.

We're only taking a piece of the virus, we're not taking the whole virus ... The first thing about [the PCR] test is, it was admitted by the U.S. Food and Drug Administration and the CDC that the tests put out by the CDC were contaminated.

And when you amplify something a million times, or 10 million times — whatever they do in the 30 cycles or so — it's logarithmic that RNA then is way overestimated ... [But] no [viral] particle was identified or isolated from your saliva or from your nasal passages. Nobody took the secretions from your nose or your mouth and isolated the [actual] viruses.

[When I isolated] HIV in 1983, I isolated it from saliva. What you do is you take the virus and grow it in any human cell, in an appropriate cell line, and you make many copies. [Viral replication] means you have [a positive test for] that virus. Then you sequence the whole virus.

A PCR [test, on the other hand] can give you a lot of false positives [by amplifying RNA fragments].

We [also] showed the people that had [HIV] infection had antibodies; that they had been fully exposed and it was not a piece of nucleic acid in a biopsy or in their throat or in their nose. [A piece of nucleic acid] is not a virus. And it's certainly not infectious.

If RNA is there and in the tiniest amount, I'm not going to cough it on somebody, especially if I'm not coughing. I'm not going to breathe that [out and infect] somebody because there's no evidence of an infectious virus."

Better Testing Strategy: Antibodies

Rather than using PCR testing, "what should have been done is test for antibodies," Mikovits says. This is what was done in South Korea. An antibody test will tell you whether you had the infection at some point, and have developed a strong immune response or immunological memory that will allow you to fight the infection should you encounter it again.

"Epidemiology is not done with PCR. In fact, Kary Mullis who invented PCR, Nobel Laureate, and others, said PCR was never intended for diagnostic testing. So that puts that to bed.

It takes nothing to develop a really good serology [i.e., antibody] test ... [It takes] a few weeks. It's pretty easy because the people who have recovered have antibodies. So, you isolate those antibodies, you take their plasma, you purify the antibodies, and then you can grow them.

Then you develop the tests... It's usually ELISA or Western Blot [which check for] the protein and the antibody binds. You form an immune complex, and you detect it with a dye. You can do that test with a finger stick ... and it takes 15 minutes to get the answer, almost like a pregnancy test."

My belief is that the use of PCR instead of a proper antibody test was intentional, as it inflates the case numbers. Mikovits agrees, saying "I wouldn't get any tests right now. I'd simply wash my hands and drink hot lemon water as I always do for any flu season."

Evidence SARS-CoV-2 May Be a Lab-Created Virus

In the Epoch Times documentary, "<u>Tracking Down the Origin of the Wuhan Coronavirus</u>," Mikovits details some of the evidence supporting the view that SARS-CoV-2 is not a naturally-evolved virus, but rather a laboratory concoction.

One piece of evidence is that the virus contains a protein envelope from the HIV virus. It's also very similar to SARS which, according to <u>bioweapons expert Francis Boyle</u>, is an engineered bioweapon.

As explained by Mikovits, an Indian paper detailed the presence of Gp120, a protein envelope from the HIV virus. (Editor Note: Paper follows this transcript). That paper was quickly retracted due to political pressure. However, Mikovits colleague, Luc Montagnier, made a similar discovery, finding Gp41 in the SARS-CoV-2 virus, which is the transmembrane domain of the HIV virus.

"The folks from India also had GAG. That's structural proteins. That gives you a clue that it wasn't a CRISPR technique or a pseudotyping where the envelope was expressed in a gene therapy-type of way. Ifit were CRISPR, you wouldn't put the GAG sequences in there.

What was done is, the virus was acquired as they grew SARS-CoV-2 in Vero-E6 cells — the monkey kidney cells where you get HIV.

Simian immune deficiency virus was the origin, and we were told all the way back in the 80s that somebody forgot to cook their food in Africa and a few promiscuous men spread this [HIV] virus around the world. So, you can see again the patterns of the lies and of what people end up believing."

The addition of this envelope protein from HIV gives SARS-CoV-2 the ability to impair the immune system. It also contributes to its pathogenicity. Mikovits continues her explanation:

"The first thing is, you must grow a virus to make a lot of it. So, you grow it in cell lines. They didn't take [SARS-CoV-2] from the bat and it jumped into a human. It normally goes through another cell [from] a monkey or a smaller animal. The cell line that supports the growth and expansion [of viruses] are monkey kidney cells.

Maybe [SARS-CoV-2] is not engineered at all ... but the end result is, now it not only infects the epithelial cells of the lungs, it infects the white blood cells, it infects the immune cells. We see the splenomegaly in large spleens, we're seeing penias, cytopenias. We're losing cells like HIV-killing T-cells ...

So, it's got not only an expanded host range, but also disease symptoms that make no sense for a coronavirus. Hence, we're killing people because they're treating an upper respiratory infection, and you're getting that inflammatory disease signature because you're infecting the very innate immune response, the macrophages, the monocytes, the natural killer cells, the T cells. And it's primarily the T-cells in the macrophages because those are the cells HIV 120 and Gp41 infect through CCR5 in the CD4 receptor.

So now you're going to lose your adaptive immune response, you're going to drive the inflammation. And it's the fire [of inflammation] that does the tissue damage."

Another piece that hints at SARS-CoV-2 being a manufactured virus is the construction of its spike proteins, which bind to ACE2 receptors to gain access into the cell. This appears to be an engineering feature. According to Mikovits, it's quite clear that the spike proteins came from the original SARS virus, which also infects through ACE receptors.

There are also "single point mutations there that make it far more infectious, easier to spread," she says, "and how those were acquired, nobody really can say." At least not yet. Nanotechnology may also have been used to aerosolize it for ease of transmission.

"The nano[size] further increases the host range. So now you can go into every cell. Now you can go across the blood brain barrier. That's nano. Now you don't need a receptor. You can breathe it, it can go into every cell of the body. You don't need the gatekeeper. You don't need the receptor. You don't need the lock and key."

Contaminated Cell Line Shared With Wuhan Biolab

According to Mikovits, one contaminated cell line is the Vero monkey kidney cell line called Vero E6, which was given by Fort Detrick — a U.S. Army Medical Command installation that hosts many of our national biological defense programs and houses the National Cancer Institute laboratory where she used to work — to the biosafety 4 laboratory (BSL-4) in Wuhan, China. This cell line is what the Wuhan lab used to grow and study coronaviruses, she says.

The Vero cell line is listed in the 2015 paper, "A SARS-like Cluster of Circulating Bat Coronaviruses Shows Potential for Human Emergence," co-written by University of North Carolina researchers and Dr. Shi Zhengli, a Chinese virologist at the Wuhan lab who in 2010 published a paper discussing the weaponization of the SARS virus.

The contaminated Vero monkey kidney cells were also used in the production of polio vaccines, Mikovits notes. The original polio vaccines were passed through mice brains, as we didn't have cell lines in the 1930s when that vaccine was originally developed. According to Mikovitz, the spread of this Vero retrovirus has occurred through laboratory workers and hospital caretakers for decades.

"That's why the family studies we did were so important," she says, referring to studies in which retroviral transmission was tracked to determine how it spread between family members.

Alas, whenever patterns were detected, she was always directed to cover them up. Her refusal to hide the information from the public was what led to her firing in 2011. According to Mikovits, we're seeing the same pattern of sweeping evidence under the rug now during the COVID-19 pandemic.

"The patterns are the same as far as the science goes, and the patterns are the same as far as the political corruption, the plague of corruption, in covering up data,"she says.

The key take-home here is that retroviruses are "integrated into the host cell genome," and infection can result in "long-term expression." In other words, once they're in your body, they can remain dormant, only to reactivate when conditions are favorable. In this regard, they're quite different from your average virus that, when you're exposed, invades your cells, replicates and causes symptoms, and is eventually eliminated from your body through your immune response.

To reiterate some of the key take-home messages Mikovits delivers in this interview:

•She believes COVID-19 — the disease — is not caused by SARS-CoV-2 alone, but rather that it's the result of a combination of SARS-CoV-2 (which appears to have been manipulated to include components of HIV that destroys immune function). Previous XMRV (human gammaretroviruses) infection may facilitate SARS-CoV-2 to express the COVID-19 illness.

Put another way, COVID-19 may be initiated by SARS-CoV-2 but dependent upon a preexisting infection with and awakening of other viruses such as XMRV, gamma retroviruses, possibly Lyme and other coinfections, including parasites, and this is why anti-parasitic medications like hydroxychloroquine and Ivermectin help.

•Blood products and vaccines are contaminated with XMRVs that can damage your immune system and cause CFS, cancer and other chronic diseases. The viruses spread within laboratories as they have adapted to become aerosolized, and contaminate cell lines used in vaccine production and other viral research, including research on coronaviruses.

•Flu vaccines have spread a host of dangerous viruses around the world, which can then interact with SARS COV-2.

•It is possible to develop safer oral vaccines, and interferon alpha could be a valuable treatment alternative against COVID-19. Aside from interferons, other treatment strategies discussed in our interview include hyperbaric oxygen therapy, cannabinoids (CBD), peptide T and antioxidant support.

•SARS-CoV-2 is more dangerous and virulent than typical coronaviruses because it includes sequences of HIV, SARS and another virus, which enable it to infect more than just your respiratory epithelium. It can also infect blood cells and hematopoeitic organs such as the spleen.

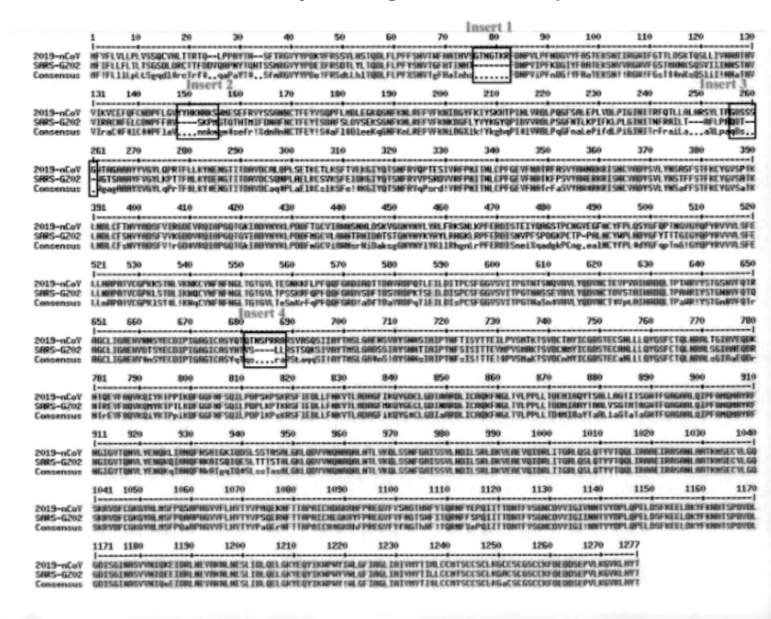

Uncanny similarity of unique inserts in the 2019-nCoV spike protein to HIV-1 gp120 and Gag

- **We retrieved all the available coronavirus sequences (n=55) from NCBI viral genome database (https://www.ncbi.nlm.nih.gov/) and we used the GISAID to retrieve all available full-length sequences (n=28) of 2019-nCoV as on 27 Jan 2020.**

- **We found four new insertions in the S protein of 2019-nCoV when compared to its nearest relative, SARS CoV.**

- **We found that these 4 insertions [inserts 1, 2, 3 and 4] are unique to 2019-nCoV and are not present in other coronaviruses analyzed.**

- **The finding of 4 unique inserts in the 2019-nCoV, all of which have identity /similarity to amino acid residues in key structural proteins of HIV-1 is unlikely to be fortuitous in nature.**

- This indicates that these insertions have been preferably acquired by the 2019-nCoV, providing it with additional survival and infectivity advantage.

- These proteins are critical for the viruses to identify and latch on to their host cells and for viral assembly.

- Since surface proteins are responsible for host tropism, changes in these proteins imply a change in host specificity of the virus. According to reports from China, there has been a gain of host specificity in case 2019-nCoV as the virus was originally known to infect animals and not humans but after the mutations, it has gained tropism to humans as well.

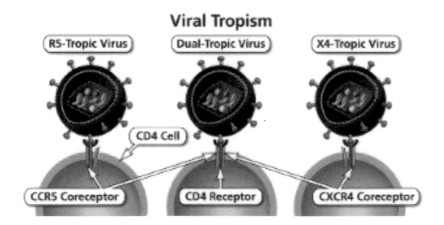

- Taken together, our findings suggest unconventional evolution of 2019-nCoV that warrants further investigation. Our work highlights novel evolutionary aspects of the 2019-nCoV and has implications on the pathogenesis and diagnosis of this virus.

The Coronavirus Is Man Made According to Luc Montagnier the Man Who Discovered HIV

- Contrary to the narrative that is being pushed by the mainstream that the COVID 19 virus was the result of a natural mutation and that it was transmitted to humans from bats via pangolins, Dr Luc Montagnier the man who discovered the HIV virus back in 1983 disagrees and is saying that the virus was man made.

- Professor Luc Montagnier, 2008 Nobel Prize winner for Medicine, claims that SARS-CoV-2 is a manipulated virus that was accidentally released from a laboratory in Wuhan, China. Chinese researchers are said to have used coronaviruses in their work to develop an AIDS vaccine. HIV RNA fragments are believed to have been found in the SARS-CoV-2 genome.

- According to the 2008 Nobel Prize for Medicine, a plausible explanation would be an accident in the Wuhan laboratory. He also added that the purpose of this work was the search for an AIDS vaccine.

- "With my colleague, bio-mathematician Jean-Claude Perez, we carefully analyzed the description of the genome of this RNA virus," explains Luc Montagnier, interviewed by Dr Jean-François Lemoine for the daily podcast at Pourquoi Docteur, adding that others have already explored this avenue: Indian researchers have already tried to publish the results of the analyses that showed that this coronavirus genome contained sequences of another virus, … the HIV virus (AIDS virus), but they were forced to withdraw their findings as the pressure from the mainstream was too great.

- "says Luc Montagnier," in order to insert an HIV sequence into this genome, molecular tools are needed, and that can only be done in a laboratory.

	70	80	"insert" 1	100
Consensus Identity	QDLFLP FYSNVTWFHXINVS - - - - - XXIFDNPVLP FKDGXIYFAATE			
1. 2019-nCoV/human/Wuhan-Hu-1	QDLFLP FFSNVTWFHAIHVS GTNGTKR FDNPVLP FNDGVYFASTE			
2. 2019-nCoV/human/USA-WA1/2020	QDLFLP FFSNVTWFHAIHVS GTNGTKR FDNPVLP FNDGVYFASTE			
3. 2019-nCoV/human/USA-CA2/2020	QDLFLP FFSNVTWFHAIHVS GTNGTKR FDNPVLP FNDGVYFASTE			
4. SARS-like/bat/Yunnan/RaTG13/2013	QDLFLP FFSNVTWFHAIHVS GTNGIKR FDNPVLP FNDGVYFASTE			
5. SARS-like/bat/SL-CoVZXC21	QGYFLP FYSNVSWYYSLTTN - NAATKR TDNP ILD FKDGIYFAATE			
6. SARS-like/bat/SL-CoVZC45	QGYFLP FYSNVSWYYSLTTN - NAATKR TDNP ILD FGDGIYFAATE			
7. SARS-like/bat/HKU3-6	QDYFLP FDSNLTQYFSLNWD - SDRYTY FDNP ILD FGDGVYFAATE			
8. SARS-like/bat/LYRa11	QDLFLP FNSNVVGLMSFNYR - - - - - FDNP IIPFKDGVYFAATE			
9. SARS-like/bat/Rs4255	QDYFLP FDTNLTRYLSFNMD - SATKVY FDNPTLP FGDGIYFAATE			
10. SARS-like/bat/WIV1	QDHFLP FDSNVTRFITFGLN - - - - - FDNP IIPFKDGIYFAATE			
11. SARS-like/bat/Rs4874	QDLFLP FYSNVTGFHTINHR - - - - - FDNPVIP FKDGVYFAATE			
12. SARS/human/GZ02	QDLFLP FYSNVTGFHTINHT - - - - - FDNPVIP FKDGIYFAATE			
13. SARS/human/TW4	QDLFLP FYSNVTGFHTINHT - - - - - FGNPVIP FKDGIYFAATE			
14. SARS/human/ZJ0301	QDLFLP FYSNVTGFHTINHT - - - - - FGNPVIP FKDGIYFAATE			

Glossary of Terms

Adeno-associated viruses

Adeno-associated viruses(AAV) are small viruses that infect humans and some other <u>primate species</u>.

AAV are not currently known to cause disease. The viruses cause a very mild immune response. Several additional features make AAV an attractive candidate for creating viral vectors for gene therapy, and for the creation of isogenic human disease models. Gene therapy vectors using AAV can infect both dividing and quiescent cells and persist in an extrachromosomal state without integrating into thegenomeof the host cell, although in the native virus integration of virally carried genes into the host genome does occur.

Antigen

In immunology, an antigen (Ag) is a molecule or molecular structure, such as may be present at the outside of a pathogen, that can be bound to by an antigen-specific antibody (Ab) or B cell antigen receptor(BCR).

The presence of antigens in the body normally triggers an <u>immune response</u>.

Antigens are "targeted" by antibodies. Each antibody is specifically produced by the immune system to match an antigen after cells in the immune system come into *contact* with it; this allows a precise identification or matching of the antigen and the initiation of a <u>tailored response</u>.

Also, an antigen is a molecule that binds to Ag-specific receptors, but cannot necessarily induce an immune response in the body by itself. Antigens are usually proteins, peptides (amino acid chains) and polysaccharides (chains of monosaccharides/simple sugars) but lipids and nucleic acids become antigens only when combined with proteins and polysaccharides.

The antigen may originate from within the body ("self-antigen") or from the external environment ("non-self").

Vaccines are examples of antigens in an immunogenic form, which are intentionally administered to a recipient to induce the memory function of the adaptive immune system toward the antigens of the pathogen invading that recipient.

Complementary DNA

n. Abbr. cDNASingle-stranded DNA synthesized in the laboratory using messenger RNA as a template and the enzyme reverse transcriptase.

Complementary DNA - single-stranded DNA that is complementary to messenger RNA or DNA that has been synthesized from messenger RNA by reverse transcriptase

DNA Vaccines

DNA vaccine work began thirty years ago, but as yet there are no licensed DNA vaccines and most remain in Phase 1 testing.

The key challenge associated with DNA vaccines is that they must penetrate the cell nucleus (crossing two membranes; the cytoplasm and the nucleus). The DNA must then be transcribed in the nucleus into mRNA before moving to the cytoplasm to stimulate antigen production.

Once inside the nucleus, DNA vaccines have a risk of permanently changing a person's DNA.

RNA Vaccine

An RNA vaccine or mRNA vaccine is a new type of vaccine for providing acquired immunity through an RNA-containing vector, such as lipid nanoparticles.

Just like normal vaccines, RNA vaccines are intended to induce the production of antibodies which will bind to potential pathogens. The RNA sequence codes for antigens, proteins that are identical or resembling those of the pathogen. Upon the delivery of the vaccine into the body, this sequence is translated by the host cells to produce the encoded antigens, which then stimulate the body's adaptive immune system to produce antibodies against the pathogen.

Exogenous DNA

Exogenous DNA is DNA originating outside the organism of concern or study.

The introduction of exogenous DNA into a cell is called transformation (transfection in animal cells). This can take place naturally or artificially. Methods of artificial transfection include (a) chemical methods, including calcium phosphate precipitation, DEAE-dextran complexation and lipid-mediated DNA transfer; (b) physical methods, including electroporation, microinjection, and biolistic particle delivery (gene gun); and (c) using recombinant, lab manipulated viruses as vectors.

GAG

Group-specific antigen, orgag, is thepolyproteinthat contains the core structural proteins of anOrtervirus(except*Caulimoviridae*). It was named as such because scientists used to believe it was antigenic. Now it is known that it makes up the inner shell, not the envelope exposed outside. It makes up all the structural units of viral conformation and provides supportive framework for mature virion.

Genome

In the fields of molecular biology and genetics, a genome is the genetic material of an organism. It consists of DNA (or RNA in RNA viruses). The genome includes both the genes (the coding regions) and the noncoding DNA,[1] as well as mitochondrial DNA and chloroplast DNA. The study of the genome is called genomics.

Nuclear transport

Nuclear transport refers to the mechanisms by which molecules move across the nuclear membrane of a cell. The entry and exit of large molecules from the cell nucleus is tightly controlled by the nuclear pore complexes (NPCs). Although small molecules can enter the nucleus without regulation, macromolecules such as RNA and proteins require association with transport factors known as nuclear transport receptors, like karyopherins called importins to enter the nucleus and exportins to exit.

Messenger RNA (mRNA)

Messenger RNA (mRNA) is a single-stranded RNA molecule that is complementary to one of the DNA strands of a gene. The mRNA is an RNA version of the gene that leaves the cell nucleus and moves to the cytoplasm where proteins are made. During protein synthesis, an organelle called a ribosome moves along the mRNA, reads its base sequence, and uses the genetic code to translate each three-base triplet, or codon, into its corresponding amino acid.

Nucleic Acid Vaccines

Nucleic acid vaccines, DNA and messenger RNA (mRNA), deliver the nucleotide sequence (eg, "AAAGGCC...") that codes for the proteins that pathogens use to cause disease. The idea is that those proteins will act as antigens that the immunce system will recognize. In other words, these vaccines enable the body to innately mimic a native infection to elicit an immunce response, but without the ability to cause disease or spread.

Ortervirales

Ortervirales is an order that contains all accepted species of single-stranded RNA viruses that replicate through a DNA intermediate (Group VI) and all accepted species of double-stranded DNA viruses that replicate through an RNA intermediate (Group VII). The name is derived from the reverse of retro.

All reverse-transcribing viruses possess significant similarities to each other. Their reverse transcriptase proteins share a common origin. Moreover, belpaoviruses, metaviruses, pseudoviruses, and retroviruses have other features in common. Their polymerase proteins are similar in structure and include aspartic protease (retroviral aspartyl protease) and an integrase belonging to the DDE recombinase superfamily.

Polymerase

A polymerase is an enzyme that synthesizes long chains of polymers or nucleic acids. DNA polymerase and RNA polymerase are used to assemble DNA and RNA molecules, respectively, by copying a DNA template strand using base-pairing interactions or RNA by half ladder replication.

Polymerase chain reaction

Polymerase chain reaction (PCR) is a method widely used to rapidly make millions to billions of copies of a specific DNA sample, allowing scientists to take a very small sample of DNA and amplify it to a large enough amount to study in detail.

Using PCR, copies of very small amounts ofDNA sequences are exponentially amplified in a series of cycles of temperature changes. PCR is now a common and often indispensable technique used in medical laboratory and clinical laboratory research for a broad variety of applications including biomedical research and criminal forensics.

Provirus

A provirusis a virus genome that is integrated into the DNAof a host cell.

This state can be a stage of virus replication, or a state that persists over longer periods of time as either inactive viral infections or an endogenous viral element. In inactive viral infections the virus will not replicate itself except through replication of its host cell. This state can last over many host cell generations.

Endogenous retroviruses are always in the state of a provirus. When a (nonendogenous) retrovirus invades a cell, the RNA of the retrovirus is reverse-transcribed into DNA by reverse transcriptase, then inserted into the host genome by an integrase.

A provirus does not directly make new DNA copies of itself while integrated into a host genome in this way. Instead, it is passively replicated along with the host genome and passed on to the original cell's offspring; all descendants of the infected cell will also bear proviruses in their genomes. This is known aslysogenic viral reproduction. Integration can result in a latent infection or a productive infection. In a productive infection, the provirus is transcribed into messenger RNA which directly produces new virus, which in turn will infect other cells via the lytic cycle.

Recombinant

Recombinant DNA (rDNA) molecules are DNA molecules formed by laboratory methods of genetic recombination (such as molecular cloning) to bring together genetic material from multiple sources, creating sequences that would not otherwise be found in the genome.

Recombinant DNA is the general name for a piece of DNA that has been created by combining at least two strands.

Retrovirus

Retrovirus is a type of virus that uses RNA as its genetic material. After infecting a cell, a retrovirus uses an enzyme called reverse transcriptase to convert its RNA into DNA. The retrovirus then integrates its viral DNA into the DNA of the host cell, which allows the retrovirus to replicate. HIV, the virus that causes AIDS, is a retrovirus.

Reverse transcriptase

A reverse transcriptase (RT) is an enzyme used to generate complementary DNA (cDNA) from an RNA template, a process termed reverse transcription. Reverse transcriptases are used by retroviruses to replicate their genomes, by retrotransposon mobile genetic elements to proliferate within the host genome, by eukaryotic cells to extend the telomeres at the ends of their linear chromosomes, and by some non-retroviruses such as the hepatitis B virus, a member of the *Hepadnaviridae*, and SARS-Cov-2, a member of the *Coronaviridae* family.

Retroviral

Retroviral RT has three sequential biochemical activities: RNA-dependent <u>DNA polymerase</u> activity, <u>ribonuclease H</u> (RNAse H), and DNA-dependent DNA polymerase activity. Collectively, these activities enable the enzyme to convert single-stranded RNA into double-stranded cDNA. In retroviruses and retrotransposons, this cDNA can then integrate into the host genome, from which new RNA copies can be made via host-cell <u>transcription</u>. The same sequence of reactions is widely used in the laboratory to convert RNA to DNA for use in <u>molecular cloning</u>, <u>RNA sequencing</u>, <u>polymerase chain reaction</u> (PCR), or <u>genome analysis</u>.

Note: *A few viruses can alter the host genetic codes, causing even bigger problems. One notorious example is HIV. HIV is a retrovirus, which reverse transcribes the viral RNA into a piece of DNA and incorporates into the host chromosome. Once incorporated, the viral DNA (aka provirus) becomes a permanent part of the host cells, which is why HIV is incurable and patients need to take ARV for the rest of their lives.*

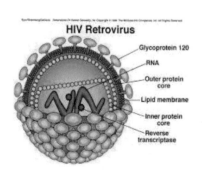

HIV Retrovirus
- Glycoprotein 120
- RNA
- Outer protein core
- Lipid membrane
- Inner protein core
- Reverse transcriptase

Transfection

Transfection is the process of deliberately introducing naked or purified nucleic acids into eukaryotic cells. It may also refer to other methods and cell types, although other terms are often preferred: "transformation" is typically used to describe non-viral DNA transfer in bacteria and non-animal eukaryotic cells, including plant cells. In animal cells, transfection is the preferred term as transformation is also used to refer to progression to a cancerous state (carcinogenesis) in these cells. Transduction is often used to describe virus-mediated gene transfer into eukaryotic cells.

The word *transfection* is a portmanteau of *trans-* and *infection*. Genetic material (such as supercoiled plasmid DNA or siRNA constructs), or even proteins such as antibodies, may be transfected.

Transfection of animal cells typically involves opening transient pores or "holes" in the cell membrane to allow the uptake of material. Transfection can be carried out using calcium phosphate (i.e. tricalcium phosphate), by electroporation, by cell squeezing or by mixing a cationic lipid with the material to produce liposomes that fuse with the cell membrane and deposit their cargo inside.

Transfection can result in unexpected morphologies and abnormalities in target cells.

How DNA of the Nucleus is changed: Transfection

Video

Tro•pism

*n.*The turning or bending movement of an organism or a part of an organism in a particular direction in response to an external stimulus such as light or gravity.*n.*

In *biology*, growth, bending, orientation, or locomotion of organisms, or of parts of organisms, in relation to external agents.*n.*

In a stricter use, the growing or bending of organisms, or of parts of organisms, in relation to external agents.

4 Main Strategies of Vaccine Development

1. Weakened Viruses (typically season flu, made from eggs)

2. Proteins (ACE2 Receptors of Covid-19) Companies: Senofi, GSK

3. Viral Vectors/Adenovirus Vector (Inactive Virus ie. common cold) (Insert genetic code of spike protein) Company: Johnson & Johnson

4. Genetic Codes (of spike protein) mRNA Companies: Inovio, Pfizer, Moderna

Draft landscape of COVID-19 candidate vaccines

166 candidate vaccines in clinical evaluation

Note: The simple fact that 166 candidate vaccines are under "warp speed" development of a vaccine, is indicative of planning years in advance of the December, 2019 public announcement of the SARS-CoV2 now referred to simply as Covid-19.

How Viruses Access The Nucleus

Many viruses, including most DNA viruses and some RNA viruses, depend on nuclear proteins for replication; therefore, their viral genome must enter the nucleus of the host cell.

Two general mechanisms have been described for nuclear import: passive diffusion and facilitated translocation. Passive diffusion is for ions and molecules smaller than 9 nm in diameter or proteins smaller than 40 kDa, whereas facilitated nuclear import can accommodate the transport of molecules with diameters of up to 39 nm [12]. The facilitated nuclear import mechanism requires a signal residing on the imported molecule (or cargo), and cytoplasmic receptors (called nuclear import receptors, importins, or karyopherins) that recognize the signal and mediate the translocation of the cargo through the NPC (Nuclear Pore Complex)

The general current understanding is that viruses deliver their genome into the nucleus of their host cells by using the machinery that evolved for the nuclear import of cellular proteins (i.e., NPCs, NLSs, importins, GTP, and Ran).

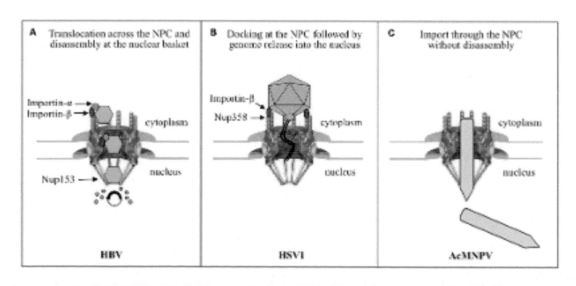

Because the size and structure of viruses vary enormously (for example, herpesviruses are 180–225 nm in diameter, but parvoviruses are 18–26 nm in diameter and because there are several nuclear import pathways, each virus has evolved a unique strategy to deliver its genome into the nucleus.

Some viruses, such as human immunodeficiency virus 1 (HIV-1) and influenza A virus, undergo extensive disassembly in the cytoplasm. The cytoplasmic released components contain NLSs and are thereby able to cross the NPC using the host transport machinery.

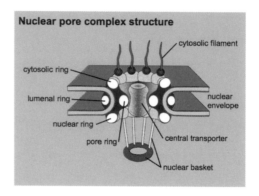

Although much progress has been made in characterizing the general nuclear entry strategies of different viruses, many of the molecular details remain obscure. The study of viral nuclear entry is complicated by the fact that viral proteins may enter the nucleus multiple times during the virus life-cycle: both as part of an incoming capsid or nucleoprotein, and perhaps also as a newly synthesized protein if assembly of progeny virions occurs in the nucleus.

Viral entry into the nucleus and genome release are part of an intricate dance between the virus and host cell, many details of which remain to be elucidated.

Retroviruses are RNA viruses which reverse transcribe their RNA genomes into DNA; the DNA is then integrated into the host genome, where it serves as a template for the synthesis of new RNA genomes. Retroviruses may enter the cell either by direct fusion of the viral envelope at the cell surface, or by fusion after internalization using an endocytic route.

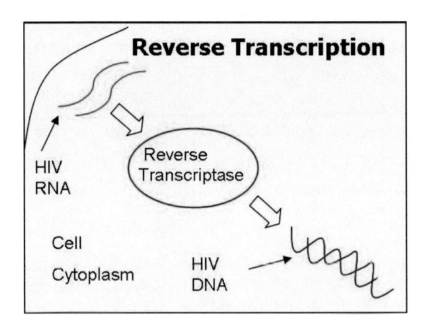

Fusion results in the release of the viral nucleoprotein core particle into the cytoplasm. This is followed by a poorly understood uncoating step and the formation of the reverse transcription complex, which for MLV includes the viral RNA genome, reverse transcriptase, integrase and the capsid protein. Reverse transcription of RNA to DNA produces the pre-integration complex (PIC), which enters the nucleus to integrate into the host genome.

While similar in many ways to MLV, lentiviruses such as HIV-1 are able to infect terminally differentiated cells in the absence of cell division. HIV-1 entry into cells is similar to the process described above for MLV, although the composition of the resulting PIC is somewhat different. While the MLV PIC includes reverse transcriptase, integrase and the capsid protein, the HIV-1 PIC is composed of reverse transcriptase, integrase, matrix protein, and the accessory protein Vpr, with the capsid protein largely dissociating prior to nuclear entry.

It is generally agreed that the HIV-1 PIC enters the nucleus by active transport through the NPC, but the molecular mechanism remains poorly understood.

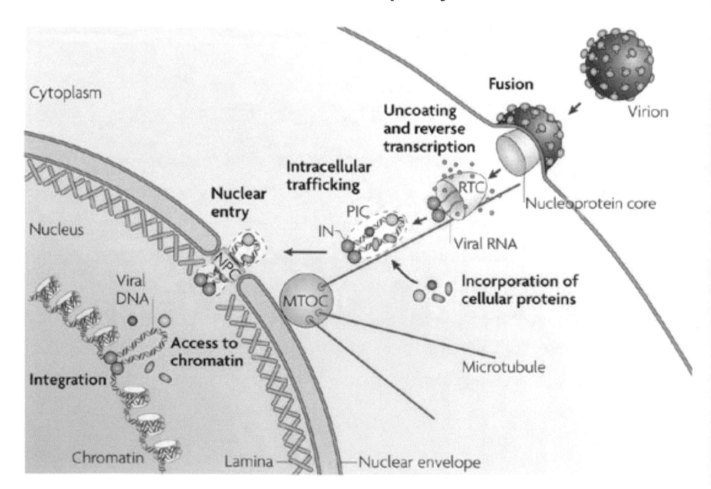

Every component of the HIV-1 PIC has been suggested to participate in mediating its nuclear entry (reviewed in). Matrix contains NLS-like sequences which target fusion proteins to the nucleus. Vpr contains an atypical NLS, and also interacts directly with Nups. In addition, Vpr has been suggested to mediate nuclear entry of the PIC via disruption of the host NE. Integrase contains several putative NLSs, and interacts directly with Nup.

In addition, a 99-bp triple-strand DNA structure in the centre of the viral DNA called the central polypurine tract (cPPT) or central DNA flap has also been suggested to participate in nuclear entry of the PIC. The cPPT has also been proposed to play a role in uncoating of the viral genome, since DNA flap-defective virions failed to disassemble both in infected cells and in an *in vitro* uncoating assay.

Of the viruses that release their genomes in the cytoplasm prior to nuclear entry, the nuclear import of influenza A virus is probably the best studied.

The influenza A virus is an enveloped virus, containing a segmented genome consisting of eight single-stranded negative-sense RNAs. While most RNA viruses replicate in the cytoplasm, influenza replication takes place in the nucleus, likely due to the requirement for cellular splicing machinery present there.

Concluding remarks

Evidently, viruses have evolved a wide variety of strategies to invade the host cell nucleus. This allows the virus to make use of the cell's machinery for DNA replication and transcription. Virus trafficking and nuclear entry is also intimately linked with virion disassembly. In addition to using the cell's DNA replication machinery, viruses take advantage of compartmentalized cellular cues to ensure that genome release occurs at the correct time.

Thus, in addition to cues such as acidification of endosomes, viruses also use binding to NPC proteins, importins or nuclear proteins to trigger genome release.

The different nuclear entry strategies used by viruses depend largely on the size and structure of the virus, and have advantages and disadvantages. The strategy used by MLV – entry during mitosis when the barrier of the NE is absent – has the disadvantage of restricting the virus to infection of dividing cells. Meanwhile, HIV-1 and influenza A undergo extensive disassembly in the cytoplasm. This is likely because the structure of the influenza virion is such that the component released upon viral envelope fusion with the endosomal membrane is a compact and stable vRNP; similarly, it seems that the retroviral PIC must form in the cytoplasm.

The consequence is that for both these viruses, the resulting nucleoprotein complex is small enough to traverse the NPC using the host transport machinery. In contrast, for herpesviruses and adenoviruses, the viral component released to the cytoplasm is a large, relatively stable icosahedral capsid. Since the capsid is too large to traverse the NPC, docking occurs at the NPC cytoplasmic side. In both cases, interaction with the NPC is used as a cue to trigger genome release. However, in the case of HSV-1 this involves ejection of the genome from an intact capsid, while the adenovirus capsid disassembles completely. Viruses such as HBV have capsids small enough to traverse the NPC intact. This strategy has the advantage that viral genomes are protected from detection and degradation in the cytoplasm. However, having entered the nucleus intact, disassembly must occur in the nucleus.

For HBV, binding at the nuclear side of the NPC serves as a cue for genome release. Lastly, parvoviruses seem to enter the nucleus by inducing disruption of the NE. It is currently puzzling what the advantages might be for a virus to use a nuclear entry strategy that involves disruption of the NE. It is possible that NE disruption results in localized changes in the compartmentalization of cellular proteins in a way that is beneficial for the virus, e.g. cytoplasmic proteins used by the virus for a replication or assembly step are able to leak into the nucleus.

It is also possible that disruption of the ONM, which is continuous with the ER, results in release of calcium and that subsequent signaling plays a role in infection.

While significant progress has been made in understanding the general nuclear entry mechanisms used by viruses, much remains to be done. It has become evident that different viruses use different host nuclear import pathways, and viral genomes gain access to the nucleus of their host cells, not only by using the cellular nuclear import machinery, but also components of other cellular pathways, such as proteins of the apoptotic machinery.

It is also evident that even viruses using the classical nuclear import receptors have evolved mechanisms to adjust the cell machinery for their needs. Although we now know more about how viruses access the nucleus, many molecular details, such as which viral NLSs are exposed at different times during infection, which viral protein interacts with cellular components, and which host transport factors are involved in each step, remain to be elucidated.

The nuclear delivery of viral genomes is an important field in virology. Discoveries in this field may lead to the development of novel classes of antiviral drugs. We imagine that in the future both viral NLSs and host transport factors could be successfully targeted to limit viral infection and reduce human disease.

Excerpts:

DNA from the vaccine has to go in the

0:14

nucleus because that's where it's made

0:15

into RNA there's no machinery to make it

0:18

o RNA in the cell membrane in the

0:20

ytoplasm so it does go into the nucleus

0:23

hus it is a genetically modification of

0:27of our own bodies

this is on the PubMed website from the

12:45

you know Library of Medicine and here it

12:49

says members of the family ad know Verde

12:52

which isadenoviruses are non-enveloped

12:55

blah blah blahthat replicate in the

12:57

nucleus so once again they're basically

13:01

using the genetic sequence from this

13:04

virus to target it to the nucleus so now

13:08

we have two separate types of evidence

13:10

to show that this is actually the

13:12strategy with DNA vaccines

and you just showed two sources

14:14

from legitimate sources that actually

14:18

say exactly what this does I mean is

14:20

that injecting they're injecting DNA

14:22

right our DNA or RNA into the nucleus

14:25

essentiallyyeah these examples are

14:27

specifically DNA which is the most

14:29common strategy that's being attempted

but there are essentially a

15:07

number of technologies that are

15:09

available some on the cutting edge and

15:12

some have been around for a long time of

15:14

how they could use this type of strategy

15:17

to really do some harm and alter us even

15:21

more permanently because even with the

15:24

DNA going into the nucleus if that cell

divides then that DNA will be in the

15:30

daughter cell but it won't be in the

15:33

offspring

so in other words if you get the vaccine

15:36

and then you have children your children

15:38

won't have this far in DNA but they do

15:41

have a technology and I'll share my

15:43

screen again here so we can see called

15:46

the CRISPR technology and sorry it's

15:50

actually called gene drives and it's

15:53

it's based on the CRISPR technology and

15:56

some people may have heard of this what

15:57

a CRISPR is is it's a specific sequence

16:02

of genetic material that's derived from

16:04

a bacteria that can go into a specific

16:08

location in our chromosomes and

16:11

basically cut out the gene that's there

16:14

and replace it with whatever it's

16:16

attached to and this caste 9 is an

16:20

enzyme that helps carry that out

this is a way to sort of permanently

19:35

genetically modify us and this

19:37

technology has been developed and it's

19:40 seems like it's ready for deployment

Transcript of Dr. Carrie Madej
7/18/2020

https://youtu.be/dBvY9x2Nma0

and then what if our DNA is modified

05:58

with genes from another species are we

06:01

still human

06:02

as this transhumanism and then what if

06:06

our DNA our genome is modified and thus

06:08

can be patented and owned this is not a

06:11

sci-fi movie or future event this is

06:13

right now today this is called

06:16

recombinant DNA and recombinant RNA

06:18

technology and this is what is proposed

06:20

for Cova 19 vaccine the corona virus

06:24

Cobra 19 vaccines are designed to make

06:26

us into genetically modified organisms

COVID VACCINES BY DR. CARRIE MADEJ

that is the same lingo and terminology

06:32

used for Monsanto seeds okay so the

06:37

frontrunners for this recombinant DNA

06:39

technology are inovio

06:40

which is backed by the Gates Foundation

06:44

GlaxoSmithKline and Sanofi also moderna

06:49

is in there too now but that's also

06:52

agates backed foundation I will add that

06:55

this type of DNA vaccine has never been

06:57

used on humans before let me repeat that

07:01

please understand this has never ever

07:03been used on humans before never

they

07:08

are now proposing to take something

07:10

we've never used and to inject it into

07:12

everyone vaccine trials are being

07:15

fast-tracked at a level and a rate that

07:18

I have never seen in my life nor did I

07:21

ever expect to see this

07:22

they are skipping over the animal trials

07:24

going directly to human trials they are

07:28

not using good scientific methodology at

07:30

all

07:30

they have no randomized

07:32

placebo-controlled trials for any

07:34

vaccine which is the gold standard for

07:36

any therapy to be approved by the FDA

07:38

they're not following any sound

07:41

scientific protocol to make sure this is

07:44

safe for us to make sure it would work

07:46

for us to know anything about it and

07:48

they want to inject it into everybody

07:51

the vaccine manufacturers in general are

07:55

actually exempt from product liability

07:57

meaning if it causes seizures paralysis

07:59

etc they don't as a group are liable

08:03

okay they also exempted from randomized

08:06

control trials

08:07

they're doing this with the Cova 19

08:10vaccine

but they're also doing this with

08:12

other vaccines recently where they can

08:14

just say well we've had the MMR vaccine

08:16

before we don't need to do that you

08:18

might have tweeted a little bit it's

08:20

still the same thing well kind of you

08:23

know mindset is that I can't believe it

08:25

because just a little change can make a

08:27

big difference also they're exempted

08:29

from needing evidence to prove that

08:31

these things will do what they say they

08:32

will do so for instance they just have

08:37

to prove that the vaccine is producing

08:40

antibodies okay

08:42

just because you've antibodies does not

08:44

make you immune to something we don't

08:46

know that for a fact we don't know if it

08:48

really would work out in the population

08:50of people

a real study couldn't study

08:53

would show that it actually works in the

08:55

population of people they're not doing

08:57

that they say they don't have time so

09:00

may not work at all okay so let's ask

09:03ourselves what is the purpose

senseso let's go back to the

12:50

topic of why the vaccines are being

12:53

pushed so heavily on us if the current

12:55

research and evidence for using them is

12:57

flawed so let's follow the money and

13:00

that usually will give you some better

13:02

ideas so in 2011 the German company cure

vac was it was given 33 million dollars

13:10

for their research and development of

13:12RNA vaccines

then in 2015 inovio was given

13:25

45 million for their DNA vaccines which

13:28

they also mention admitting to using DNA

13:31

nanotechnology nanotechnology is using

13:35

microscopic

13:37

very tiny little robotic organisms okay

13:42

all of these companies are backed by the

13:46

Gates Foundation or have been associated

13:49

with the Gates Foundation in some way

13:51

it's important to note that so far these

13:54

companies have been unable to get these

13:57

products license for human use due to

13:59

the fact that these vaccines have failed

14:02

to provide sufficient immunity in human

14:04

trials sufficient immunity is again only

14:08

stating that you have a certain amount

14:10

of antibodies this again is not showing

14:13

that the person is completely immune out

14:16

in the public

- whatever virus they're trying or

14:20

bacteria they're trying to protect you

14:21

from it's only looking

14:23

in in vitro in a test-tube how many

14:27

antibodies this is not good science yet

14:30

to prove the efficacy of these vaccines

14:32even if they could get this

in 2010

14:36

DARPA which is the Pentagon's Defense

14:39

Advanced Research Projects Agency

14:42

military agency is folk started focusing

14:45

on DNA and RNA vaccines and they had a

14:48

synthetic DNA vaccine that could be

14:50

delivered via non-invasive

14:52

electroporation which is using kind of a

14:55

sticker with micro needles in it on your

14:58

skin you can barely feel it go in there

14:59

and in their words and quotations it is

this15:03

is to enhance and subvert and of

15:07

quotations humans at a genetic level

15:10

this is around the same year Bill Gates

15:12

heavily started to fund the DNA RNA

15:14

vaccines with the companies mentioned

15:16

before

Biocompatible Near-infrared Quantum Dots Delivered To The Skin by Microneedle Patches Record Vaccination

Abstract

Accurate medical recordkeeping is a major challenge in many low-resource settings where well-maintained centralized databases do not exist, contributing to 1.5 million vaccine-preventable deaths annually.

Here, we present an approach to encode medical history on a patient using the spatial distribution of biocompatible, near-infrared quantum dots (NIR QDs) in the dermis. QDs are invisible to the naked eye yet detectable when exposed to NIR light.

QDs with a copper indium selenide core and aluminum-doped zinc sulfide shell were tuned to emit in the NIR spectrum by controlling stoichiometry and shelling time. The formulation showing the greatest resistance to photobleaching after simulated sunlight exposure (5-year equivalence) through pigmented human skin was encapsulated in microparticles for use in vivo.

In parallel, microneedle geometry was optimized in silico and validated ex vivo using porcine and synthetic human skin. QD-containing microparticles were then embedded in dissolvable microneedles and administered to rats with or without a vaccine. Longitudinal in vivo imaging using a smartphone adapted to detect NIR light demonstrated that *microneedle-delivered QD patterns* remained bright and could be accurately identified using a machine learning algorithm 9 months after application.

In addition, codelivery with inactivated poliovirus vaccine produced neutralizing antibody titers above the threshold considered protective. *These findings suggest that intradermal QDs can be used to reliably encode information and can be delivered with a vaccine, which may be particularly valuable in the developing world and open up new avenues for decentralized data storage and biosensing.*

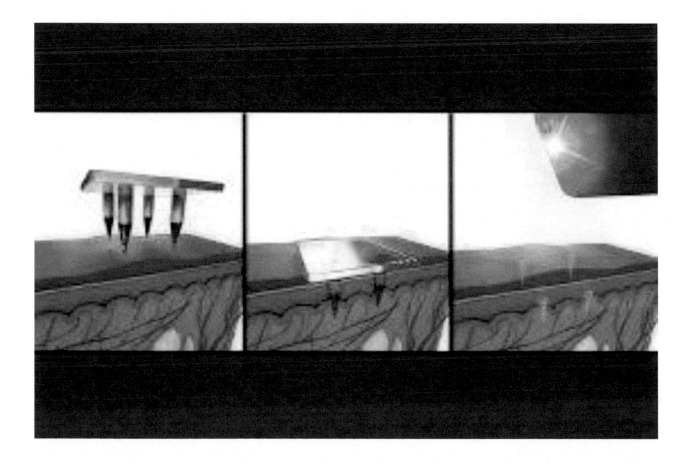

A smartphone camera was adapted with commercially available optical components purchased from Thorlabs to enhance NIR QD detection in the NIR.

To enable NIR detection, the stock short-pass IR filter was removed from a Google Nexus 5X smartphone. A smart phone case was then designed and 3D-printed to interface tightly with optical components having SM1 threading directly in front of the rear-facing camera. An 850-nm long-pass dielectric filter (FEL0850) and 850-nm long-pass color glass filter (FGL850) were placed in parallel in a lens tube attached to the smartphone case and held in place with a retaining ring.

For QD illumination, a 780-nm, 200-mW mounted LED (M780L3) powered by a T-Cube LED Driver (LEDD1B) and 15-V, 2.4-A power supply (KPS101) was used. To augment the shape and spectrum of emission, an 800-nm dielectric short-pass filter (FEL0800) and aspheric condenser lens with diffuser (ACL2520U-DG6-B) were used in an adjustable lens tube. All imaging was per-formed using the Camera FV-5 Lite app (FGAE Studios).

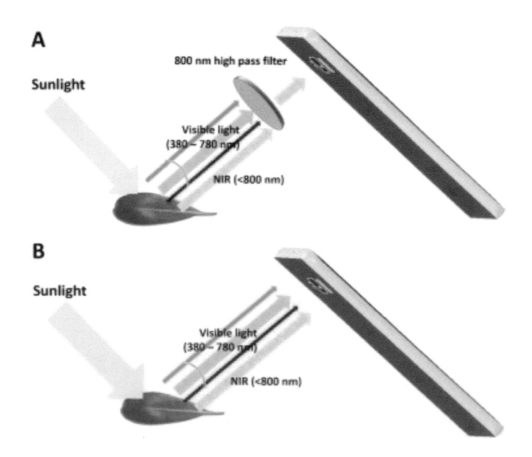

A

Sunlight

800 nm high pass filter

Visible light
(380 – 780 nm)

NIR (<800 nm)

B

Sunlight

Visible light
(380 – 780 nm)

NIR (<800 nm)

An initial discussion of QD
materials along with key concepts surrounding their
preparation and bioconjugation is
provided given the defining role these aspects play in the
QDs ability to succeed in
subsequent energy transfer (ET) applications. The
discussion is then divided around the specific roles that
QDs provide as either Forster resonance energy transfer
(FRET) or charge/electron transfer donor and/or acceptor.

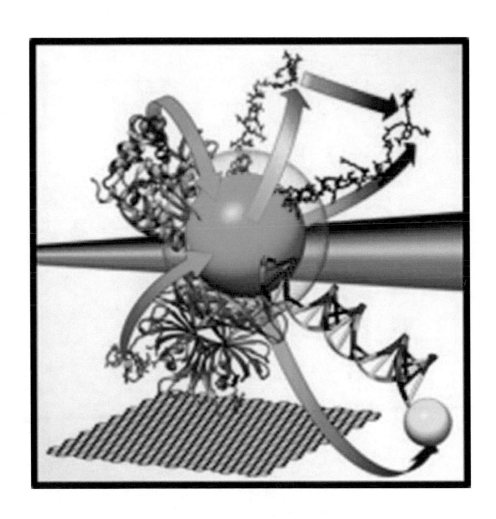

For each QD-ET mechanism, a working explanation of the appropriate background theory and formalism is articulated before examining their biosensing and related ET utility. Other configurations such as incorporation of QDs into multistep ET processes or use of initial chemical and bioluminescent excitation are treated similarly.

ET processes that are still not fully understood such as QD interactions with gold and other metal nanoparticles along with carbon allotropes are also covered. Given their maturity, some specific applications ranging from in vitro sensing assays to cellular imaging are separated and discussed in more detail. Finally a perspective on how this field will continue to evolve is provided.

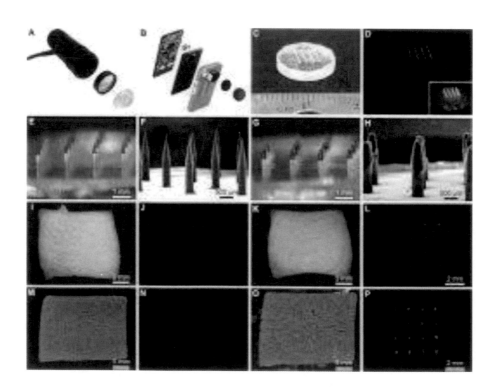

Functional Nucleic Acid-based Hydrogels for Bioanalytical and Biomedical Applications

Hydrogels are crosslinked hydrophilic polymers that can absorb a large amount of water. By their hydrophilic, biocompatible and highly tunable nature, hydrogels can be tailored for applications in bioanalysis and biomedicine. Of particular interest are DNA-based hydrogels owing to the unique features of nucleic acids.

Since the discovery of DNA double helical structure, interest in DNA has expanded beyond its genetic role to applications in nanotechnology and materials science. In particular, DNA-based hydrogels present such remarkable features as stability, flexibility, precise programmability, stimuli-responsive DNA conformations, facile synthesis and modification.

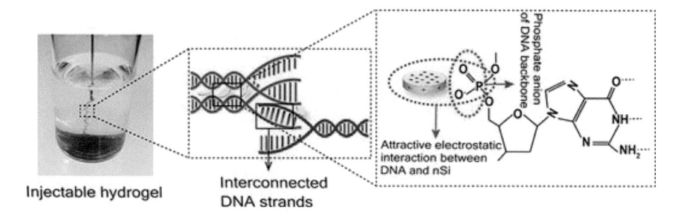

Injectable hydrogel

Interconnected DNA strands

Moreover, functional nucleic acids (FNAs) have allowed the construction of hydrogels based on aptamers, DNAzymes, i-motif nanostructures, siRNAs and CpG oligodeoxynucleotides to provide additional molecular recognition, catalytic activities and therapeutic potential, making them key players in biological analysis and biomedical applications.

To date, a variety of applications have been demonstrated with FNA-based hydrogels, including biosensing, environmental analysis, controlled drug release, cell adhesion and targeted cancer therapy. In this review, we focus on advances in the development of FNA-based hydrogels, which have fully incorporated both the unique features of FNAs and DNA-based hydrogels.

We first introduce different strategies for constructing DNA-based hydrogels. Subsequently, various types of FNAs and the most recent developments of FNA-based hydrogels for bioanalytical and biomedical applications are described with some selected examples. Finally, the review provides an insight into the remaining challenges and future perspectives of FNA-based hydrogels.

NHGRI Researchers Generate Complete Human X Chromosome Sequence

Excerpts:

Of the 24 human chromosomes (including X and Y), study authors Phillippy and Karen Miga, Ph.D., at the University of California, Santa Cruz, chose to complete the X chromosome sequence first, due to its <u>link with a myriad of diseases</u>, including hemophilia, chronic granulomatous disease and Duchenne muscular dystrophy.

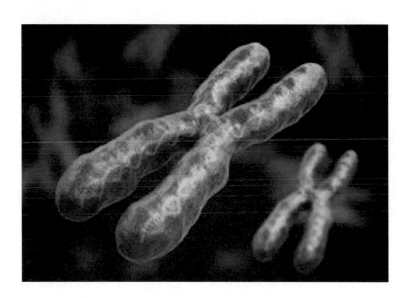

Humans have two sets of chromosomes, one set from each parent. For example, biologically female humans inherit two X chromosomes, one from their mother and one from their father. However, those two X chromosomes are not identical and will contain many differences in their DNA sequences.

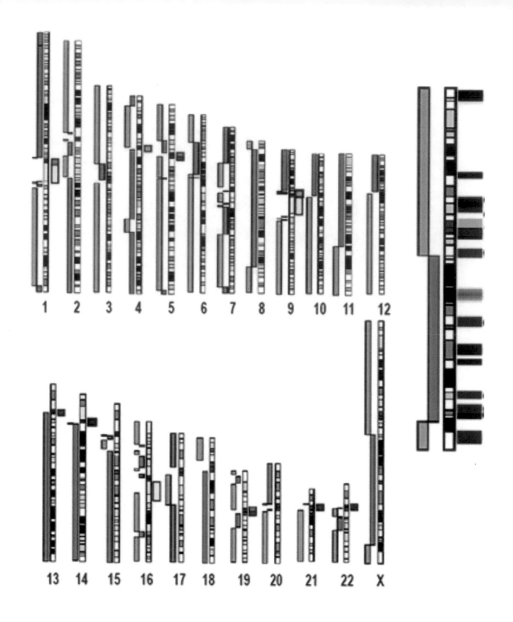

1 2 3 4 5 6 7 8 9 10 11 12

13 14 15 16 17 18 19 20 21 22 X

In this study, researchers did not sequence the X chromosome from a normal human cell. Instead, they used a special cell type – one that has two identical X chromosomes. Such a cell provides more DNA for sequencing than a male cell, which has only a single copy of an X chromosome. It also avoids sequence differences encountered when analyzing two X chromosomes of a typical female cell.

Johns Hopkins Experts Address COVID-19 Vaccine Challenges, Realistic Timelines (end of 2021)

Excerpts:

A reasonable timeline for wide distribution of vaccines is likely the end of 2021, according to Dr. Bar-Zeev.

"Even after we have a vaccine that works and even after we demonstrate its safety and efficacy and even after we've produced enough doses to go around, at least for the first round, we still need to get it delivered and that's going to be a big challenge," Dr. Bar-Zeev said. "What we're seeing is science live in real time. I think in the long run, that's good for science and that's good for community trust. In the short run, it leaves people feeling a little bit, say, uncomfortable."

US Biotech Firm Inovio Reports Encouraging Virus Vaccine Results

Excerpts:

Inovio's vaccine, called INO-4800, is designed to inject DNA into a person so as to set off a specific immune system response against the SARS-CoV-2 virus.

The medication is injected under the skin with a needle, then activated with a device that resembles a toothbrush, which delivers an electrical impulse for a fraction of a second, allowing the DNA to penetrate the body's cells and carry out its mission.

Report: Moderna Sets Price Range for Coronavirus Vaccine

Excerpt:

Considered by many observers to be the leader in the hunt for a coronavirus vaccine, Moderna (NASDAQ:MRNA) has apparently settled on a price for its potential blockbuster product. Citing "people familiar with talks between the company and potential buyers," the *Financial Times* reported Tuesday that the company aims to sell its vaccine at roughly $50 to $60 per two-dose treatment course.

SARS-CoV-2 Makes Changes That Cause Cells Not to Recognize It, New Findings Suggest

Excerpts:

With an alarm code, we can enter a building without bells going off. It turns out that the SARS coronavirus 2 (SARS-CoV-2) has the same advantage entering cells. It possesses the code to waltz right in.

"It's a camouflage," Dr. Gupta said. "Because of the modifications, which fool the cell, the resulting viral messenger RNA is now considered as part of the cell's own code and not foreign."

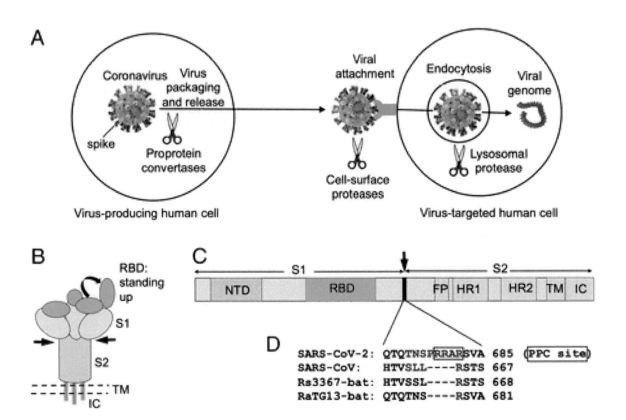

"Why a Study on Mask Effectiveness Can't Be Trusted" Dr. Tom Cowan, MD

From: "Dr. Tom Cowan" <info@humanheartcosmicheart.com>
Subject: Why a Study on Mask Effectiveness Can't Be Trusted
Date: July 28, 2020 at 12:16:31 PM CDT

If Transmission Through Exhaled Breath Hasn't Been Proven, All Other Findings Are Irrelevant

Dear friends, People around the world are being led into an increasingly downtrodden and disease-laden state, not by some viral infection but by wildly unscientific "science." A study published in the April 2020 Nature magazine that reports that wearing masks can slow the spread of the virus is an example of such deception.

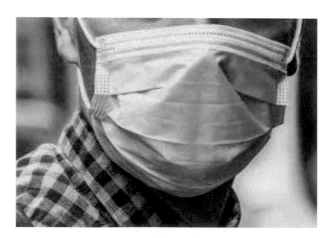

As I will show, the authors of this article repeatedly make unsupportable claims, and even present data that cast doubt on their own methodology. The peer reviewers of Nature apparently didn't catch these obvious contradictions. Let's look in some detail at the statements and claims (in italics below) in this paper.

"We found that the majority of participants with influenza virus and coronavirus infection did not shed detectable virus in respiratory droplets or aerosols."

This statement implies that the authors looked for and found detectable virus in some respiratory droplets and aerosols (but only in a minority of their subjects, who were actively sick — itself a surprising finding). It is widely known that the only way to prove the presence of a virus in a sample is to actually see the virus under electron microscopy.

There is no mention of having done any electron microscopy on any sample. When they claim they did not detect virus, what they mean is that the surrogate PCR test, which detects fragments of genetic material, was negative. However, nowhere in the medical literature is there conclusive proof that this genetic material originates from any novel virus.

"Another limitation is that we did not confirm the infectivity of coronavirus or rhinovirus detected in exhaled breath."

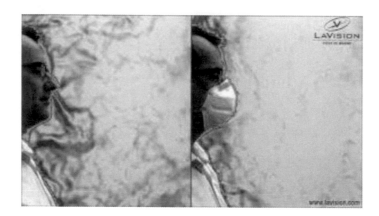

The premise of mandating the wearing of masks is that it prevents transmission of disease. Neither this study, nor any other study we've seen, proves transmission of any disease through exhaled breath.

Amazingly, these authors acknowledge they didn't even attempt to prove transmission. What's more amazing is that this study is being used as evidence that wearing masks is an effective method of preventing or lowering the incidence of disease transmission. If transmission through breath can't be proven, then all other findings in this study are rendered irrelevant.

"After one or more of the candidate respiratory viruses was detected by the viral panel from the nasal swab, all the samples from the same participant (nasal swab, throat swab, respiratory droplets and aerosols) were then tested with RT–PCR specific for the candidate virus(es) for determination of virus concentration in the samples. Infectious influenza virus was identified by viral culture using MDCK cells as described previously, whereas viral culture was not performed for coronavirus and rhinovirus."

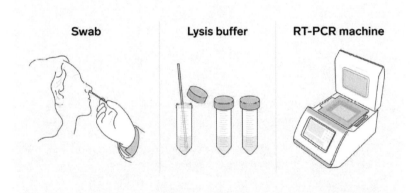

Swab   Lysis buffer   RT-PCR machine

These statements need careful examination and explanation, as they get to the core of the misleading conclusions of the study. First, they state that the method they used to detect the presence of the virus was the RT-PCR test, which, as I said, does not detect virus at all. Rather, it detects genetic material, which they only *assume* must have come from the virus in question.

Then, they say that with influenza virus, they did attempt to confirm the accuracy of the RT-PCR testing with viral "cultures." Viral culturing is itself a deceptive process, which I won't expand on here, but let's assume that it is a "gold standard" for finding the presence of "live viruses." In other words, it would be akin to doing a strep culture for someone with a sore throat. If the culture was positive, you have proof that the strep bacteria was present. (Still, the presence of the bacteria doesn't prove causation.) This positive culture allows you to check the accuracy of the rapid strep test, which detects only pieces of strep or antibodies to strep, so it confirms the validity of your surrogate test.

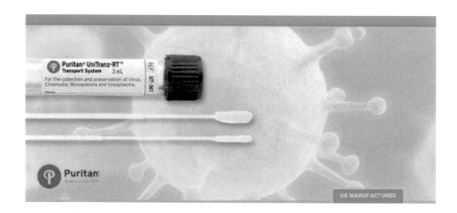

First, the study authors admit they didn't do any culturing with the coronavirus, but they did with four of the six participants who tested PCR-positive to influenza virus with droplets collected through the mask. Again, with these four participants, a very small number to be sure, they decided to do an internal check on the accuracy of their PCR testing.

What they found is only two people showed a positive culture. Even using their own flawed assumptions about viral culture, this finding demonstrates that the PCR test was falsely positive a whopping 50 percent of the time. To put this in common language, what they "proved" is that the very test they used to determine whether a mask stopped the spread of a coronavirus was no more accurate than a coin flip. Fifty percent of the time, by their own account, a positive test (for influenza virus) is incorrect, and there is no virus present.

In a sane world, this study's conclusion should have been, "Our data demonstrate that doing PCR or RT-PCR testing is an inaccurate way of detecting virus or the utility of masks to stop the spread of a virus." They then should have called for larger, carefully controlled studies to determine whether the PCR testing has any utility at all (It doesn't).

Most lay people and, incredibly, most physicians will have no idea how to read this study and determine its validity. So, people read the abstract or conclusion (or, worse yet, an article's headline, and believe what the authors assert. That is the problem. Unless someone actually helps people understand exactly what these studies are showing, and calls out the deceptive nature of much of this whole peer-reviewed science enterprise, most people will continue to be led down a path that could be disastrous personally and societally.

With gratitude for your support, and humility, please let me know whether you have questions. Tom Cowan, M.D. Human Heart Cosmic Heart 104 Villa Lane Davidson , North Carolina 28306

The following pages contain news articles and published peer-reviewed papers from science journals. These are provided as additional evidence for your own research. They are also available through my Patreon site.

Moderna, Pfizer Coronavirus Vaccines Begin Final-Stage Testing

Excerpt:

Two of the most advanced experimental coronavirus vaccines entered the pivotal phase of their studies on Monday, with the first subjects receiving doses of vaccines developed by Moderna Inc. and Pfizer Inc.

Researchers evaluating the vaccines plan to enroll 30,000 people in separate last-stage, or phase 3 trials, results of which will determine whether the vaccines protect against symptomatic Covid-19, and whether they should be cleared for widespread use.

History of Quantum Dots

Genes Silenced via Quantum Dots

Genetic Silencing Technology Improves With Help From Quantum Dots

HARVEY A. RISCH, MD, PHD , PROFESSOR OF EPIDEMIOLOGY, YALE SCHOOL OF PUBLIC HEALTH: The Key to Defeating COVID-19 Already Exists. We Need to Start Using It | Opinion

Published Paper Title:

Early Outpatient Treatment of Symptomatic, High-Risk Covid-19 Patients that Should be Ramped-Up Immediately as Key to the Pandemic Crisis

Excerpt:

As professor of epidemiology at Yale School of Public Health, I have authored over 300 peer-reviewed publications and currently hold senior positions on the editorial boards of several leading journals. I am usually accustomed to advocating for positions within the mainstream of medicine, so have been flummoxed to find that, in the midst of a crisis, I am fighting for a treatment that the data fully support but which, for reasons having nothing to do with a correct understanding of the science, has been pushed to the sidelines. As a result, tens of thousands of patients with COVID-19 are dying unnecessarily. Fortunately, the situation can be reversed easily and quickly.

Doctors Say Their COVID-19 Protocol Saves Lives. Others Want Proof.

U.S. BIOTECH FIRM: HUMAN TRIALS FOR COVID-19 VACCINE COULD BE HELD IN ISRAEL

Excerpt:

The CEO of a U.S. biotech firm with which Israel has reportedly signed a non-binding agreement for the provision of a COVID-19 vaccine said on Sunday that Phase III clinical trials for the vaccine could be conducted in the Jewish state.

Under the terms of the deal, which is reportedly worth hundreds of millions of dollars, Israel will purchase four million doses of Arcturus Therapeutics' LUNAR-COV19 vaccine candidate, which was approved for Phase I/II clinical trials in Singapore just last week, according to a report in Israel's Channel 12. The deal will only go through if the upcoming rounds of testing are successful, according to the report.

Moderna Announces Phase 3 COVE Study of mRNA Vaccine Against COVID-19 (mRNA-1273) Begins

Google Working On Smart Tattoos Turning Skin Into Living Touchpad

Link Livestream Sunday 7pm Eastern 7/26/2020: "Introduction to Three-strand DNA"

Armstrong Economics: "Vaccines That Change Your DNA Bill Gates Italian Experiment

A Very Good Essay, Written at 40,000 feet, on Covid

Link Livestream Thursday 7pm Eastern 7/23/2020: "DNA Modification"

RNA vaccines are coronavirus frontrunners

How the massive plan to deliver the COVID-19 vaccine could make history – and leverage blockchain like never before

U.S. agrees to pay Pfizer and BioNTech $2 billion for 100 million doses of coronavirus vaccine

Link Livestream 7pm Eastern 7/21/2020: "GMO Humans via Vaccine"

The Emerging Role of DNA Vaccines

Advancing Novel Experimental Gene-based COVID-19 Vaccine, AAVCOVID

Adenoviral vectors are the new COVID-19 vaccine front-runners. Can they overcome their checkered past?

Tattoo Recognition Technology - Challenge (Tatt-C)

The Present And Future Of Digital Pills
Excerpt:

Such a treatment procedure will soon be reality. 3D-printing of multiple medicines on a single pill, known as a polypill, is already a possibility. PillCam develops ingestible capsules equipped with camera systems to visualise the digestive tract. As for a trackable digital pill, Proteus Digital Health pioneered these. While these are three separate examples, it's not far-fetched to envision a company coming up with an amalgamation of these trio and offer a solution akin to the introductory story.

July 16, 2020: National Covid-19 Testing & Tracing
Action Plan (Rockefeller Foundation paper)

Rockefeller Foundation - Scenarios for the Future of
Technology and International Development

(Johns Hopkins) "The Public's Role in COVID-19
Vaccination: Planning Recommendations Informed by
Design Thinking and the Social, Behavioral, and
Communication Sciences"

FDA Grants Emergency Use Authorization for Covid-19
Pool Testing, Which Analyzes Multiple Samples at Once
Excerpt:

 Faced with the biggest coronavirus outbreak in the world and
long wait times for test results, the Food and Drug
Administration on Saturday issued the first emergency use
authorization for covid-19 pool testing, a form of testing that
allows up to four samples to be tested at once using the same
test.

Link Livestream 7pm Eastern 7/19/2020: "Not of this
World"

Couple under house arrest after testing positive for COVID-19

Excerpt:

After testing positive but without showing any symptoms, Linscott said the health department contacted her, requesting she sign documents.

"I agreed to comply to call the Health Department if I was to go. I was to call the Health Department if I was to leave my house for any reason," she said.

The World Health Organization Hired a Top PR Firm to Fight COVID Smears in The U.S.

COVID-19 vaccine may be ready by October, Pfizer CEO says

Excerpts:

The vaccine is developing quickly through a scientific method not used before. It uses the genetic blueprint of the virus, rather than a killed or weakened virus

"Once you have the genetic sequence, then you can make the RNA synthetically in the laboratory, and you can make it in pretty large amounts. You can make it pure," Garry said.

Masks Don't Work: A Review of Science Relevant to COVID-19 Social Policy

Meet The Israeli Intelligence-Linked Firm Using AI To Profile Americans And Guide US Lockdown Policy

Link Livestream 7pm Eastern 7/16/2020: "Trust"

Global Identity Verification

Mastercard Digital Wellness Program to Enhance Transparency, Security and Choice for Online Shopping

Gavi and Mastercard join forces to reach more children with lifesaving vaccines

Covid Data Collection from CDC over to HHS

Africa to Become Testing Ground for "Trust Stamp" Vaccine Record and Payment System

An mRNA Vaccine against SARS-CoV-2 — Preliminary Report - The New England Journal of Medicine - July 14, 2020

Link Livestream 7pm Eastern Sunday 7/12/2020: "WARP Speed Economic & DNA RESET"

The Current and Future State of Vaccines, Antivirals and Gene Therapies Against Emerging Coronaviruses

Biggest coronavirus vaccine deal yet: $2.1 billion to Sanofi/GSK for up to 100 million doses

Minnesota Senator Scott Jensen released this video as he is having his medical license threatened over speaking out about death certificates for C0VID

More on the patch by Patch: Coronavirus vaccine could come from California, with no shot needed

Please retain this link to ALL issues of Entangled Magazine

https://www.anthonypatch.com/entangled_subscriber_links_eo49vdfs1kb9043k.html

For more information, please join us on Patreon.

www.anthonypatch.com

Made in the USA
Coppell, TX
01 November 2020